W9-BXG-190

KERMIT: The best frog in the news-reporting business

THE CAST
OF
CHARACTERS

LADY HOLIDAY: England's star fashion designer

NICKY HOLIDAY: Lady Holiday's unsavory brother

CARLA, MARLA, and DARLA: Three ambitious models

MISS PIGGY: The most exciting new fashion model in London

THE BASEBALL DIAMOND:
Lady Holiday's prize jewel—the
largest diamond in the world

GONZO: A *Chronicle* staff
photographer with a nose for news

FOZZIE: Ace reporter, comedian,
aspiring detective

MIKE TARKANIAN: Editor-in-Chief of the *Daily Chronicle*

The GREAT MUPPET CAPER

The Storybook Based on the Movie
STARRING JIM HENSON'S MUPPETS™

Muppet Press / Random House

LORD GRADE PRESENTS

The Great Muppet Caper

A Jim Henson Film

Starring The Muppet Performers

JIM HENSON
FRANK OZ
DAVE GOELZ
JERRY NELSON
RICHARD HUNT
STEVE WHITMIRE
LOUISE GOLD
KATHRYN MULLEN

Executive Producer Martin Starger
Music and Lyrics by Joe Raposo
Written by Tom Patchett and Jay Tarses
Jerry Juhl and Jake Rose
Produced by David Lazer and Frank Oz
Directed by Jim Henson

Storybook adaptation by Jocelyn Stevenson

Library of Congress Cataloging in Publication Data:

Stevenson, Jocelyn. The great Muppet caper.
SUMMARY: Kermit, Fozzie, and Gonzo set out for London where they
and Miss Piggy search for the thief of Lady Holiday's jewels.
[1. Mystery and detective stories]
I. Title. PZ7.S8476Gr   [Fic]   81-4583
ISBN: 0-394-84874-8 (trade); 0-394-94874-2 (lib. bdg.) AACR2

Manufactured in the United States of America
3   4   5   6   7   8   9   0

Copyright © 1981 by Henson Associates, Inc.
THE GREAT MUPPET CAPER, THE MUPPET SHOW, MUPPET,
and MUPPET character names are trademarks of Henson Associates, Inc.
All rights reserved under International and Pan-American Copyright Conventions.
Published in the United States by Random House, Inc., New York,
and simultaneously in Canada by Random House of Canada Limited, Toronto.
A Muppet Press Book produced by Henson Organization Publishing
in association with Random House, Inc.

Kermit the Frog and Fozzie Bear were reporters . . . investigative reporters . . . *crack* investigative reporters. They were the best frog and bear team in the newspaper reporting business.

The Great Gonzo, who looked like a cross between a turkey and a mosquito, was their photographer. And Gonzo was *never* shy with a camera.

Kermit, Fozzie, and Gonzo had landed staff positions with the *Daily Chronicle*, a major newspaper in the big American city where they lived. When Mike Tarkanian, the editor, hired them, he said, "Okay, you guys. Get out there and cover the

news like a blanket!" So all they had to do was turn in earth-shattering, in-depth news stories, to amaze the public and sell lots of papers. And one fine spring day, they had their big chance.

Kermit and Fozzie were striding down Main Street, dodging pedestrians. Gonzo was behind them, stopping every now and then to take a photograph. All three were on the lookout for a good story. Kermit carried a pencil and notebook in his trench-coat pocket. Fozzie wore his PRESS card in his hatband. Gonzo's finger stayed close to the shutter release on his camera. If there was news nearby, they were going to find it—and today was their lucky day. Because, before their very eyes, a chicken got loose on Main Street.

"Hey, Fozzie, did you see that?" Kermit said. "Gonzo! Get a picture of the chicken!"

While Gonzo tried to take a good shot, Kermit and Fozzie chased the chicken for an interview.

Meanwhile, right across the street, an elegant woman walked out of a jewelry store. It was Lady Holiday, a famous London dress designer. She waited outside the store, impatiently tapping her foot. She looked down the street to see what was taking her chauffeur so long. She had other stops to make before flying home to England.

In the split second while her head was turned, someone snatched her handbag. Lady Holiday whirled around just in time to see a masked man dressed in black dash toward a car with her bag. She screamed "He's stolen my jewels!"

"Stop! Thief!" yelled a doorman. He started to chase the car, but the driver gunned the engine and sped off.

Across the street, Kermit, Fozzie, and Gonzo *still* hadn't photographed the chicken. They tried to corner it, but it slipped away.

The getaway car bolted down the street, charged through some garbage cans, then disappeared around a corner. The garbage cans banged into a scaffold which collapsed; the workman on the scaffold fell on top of a man walking by, knocking him to the ground and sending his bundle flying into a manhole. The bundle contained live explosives. Main Street blew up.

Kermit, Fozzie, and Gonzo missed it all.

Later, in the *Daily Chronicle* office, Mike Tarkanian was so furious the veins in his neck looked like they would burst any second. "How could you miss a story like that?" he screeched. "It practically bit you in the seat of your pants! There's no excuse!"

"I guess this is the wrong time to ask for a raise," said Fozzie.

"I'll give you a raise!" roared Tarkanian. He slammed his fist on the desk and sent Kermit, Fozzie, and Gonzo flying high into the air.

"See these headlines?" he continued, his neck getting redder with each word. " 'JEWEL HEIST ON MAIN STREET,' 'LADY HOLIDAY'S JEWELS STOLEN,' 'FASHION QUEEN OF LONDON ROBBED.' " Tarkanian paused to catch his breath.

"And last, but not least, here's *our* cute little story." He threw down a copy of the *Daily Chronicle*. The head-

9

line read: "IDENTICAL TWINS JOIN THE CHRONICLE STAFF." Underneath it was a picture of Kermit and Fozzie, taken by Gonzo.

"We thought identical twins working on a newspaper would make an interesting story," explained Kermit.

"Well it doesn't!" yelled Tarkanian. "Especially since you guys don't look anything alike!"

"We'll do better next time," promised Fozzie.

"*Next* time?" Tarkanian's eyes popped. "What makes you think there's going to be a next time? You're fired!" He picked up his clipboard and pushed past them.

Kermit, Fozzie, and Gonzo gulped. It looked as if Tarkanian was serious. "Won't you listen to reason, sir?" said Kermit, catching up with Tarkanian.

"Not a chance! This is it!" Tarka-

nian barked. "I'm not giving you your jobs back."

"We don't want you to give us anything," said Kermit. "Just pay our way to London so we can talk to Lady Holiday, the woman who was robbed. That's all you have to do."

"Oh, is that all?" said Tarkanian, wide-eyed.

"Well," said Fozzie, "we could use some new luggage for the trip. . . ."

Tarkanian slammed his fist on the desk again. "Get out of here!" he screamed as he whipped around and marched into his office.

Kermit, Fozzie, and Gonzo stared at Tarkanian's back. They were fired, no doubt about it. But that didn't matter. They would go to London anyway and interview Lady Holiday. They would find out who stole her jewels. What a story they could write then. Tarkanian would *have* to

take them back. *And* he might even give them a raise.

Kermit, Fozzie, and Gonzo were soon high over the Atlantic in a jumbo jet to England. Of course, being unemployed, they couldn't go first class. Each had his own rented cage in the cargo hold. The cages were comfortable enough, with nice bars to look out of, but they couldn't see much. It was very dark in there. Kermit listened to his fellow passengers bark, meow, tweet, wheeze, and baa. He felt as if he were trapped at night, in the dead of winter, on a flying farm.

"What do you figure, it's fifty below or what?" He shivered.

"Can you reach the hostess call button?" asked Fozzie. "I'm getting hungry."

"They don't serve food in ninth class, Fozzie," said Kermit.

Fozzie was outraged. "Twelve dollars and we don't even get a meal?"

But Gonzo was unperturbed. He peered through the bars of his cage at a paisley suitcase. "Hey, can you guys keep it down?" he said. "I'm trying to watch the movie."

Just then, a flight steward entered the hold. "All out for England!" he called.

"Oh great!" said Kermit. "The plane's landing."

"No," the steward corrected him, opening the cargo door. "The plane lands in Italy. *You* land in England." And he hurled the three cages out the door.

"Gerrrrrronnnnnnnnimmmmmmm-mmmo!" whooped Gonzo as they glided through the air.

SPLASH! Within seconds, they had landed. Kermit, Fozzie, and Gonzo slowly pushed open the doors of their cages and peeked out. They were in the middle of a pond. Nearby, children were playing cricket and a gentleman with a derby was sitting on a bench reading a newspaper.

The gentleman, hearing the splash, lowered his paper. "Ah," he said. "For once the forecast is correct. It *is* raining cats and dogs."

"No, no," protested Kermit. "We're bears and frogs."

"And Gonzos," added Gonzo.

"Well, whoever or whatever you

are, welcome to Great Britain," said the gentleman. "You've already made quite a splash," he added.

"We're on our way to London," said Kermit. "Could you recommend a nice hotel where we can stay? Actually, a *cheap* hotel."

"How cheap?" asked the gentleman.

"Free," answered Fozzie.

The gentleman thumbed through a dog-eared guidebook. "Here we are. . . . Free places to stay . . . river bank . . . bus terminal . . . Happiness Hotel . . ."

"Happiness Hotel!" interrupted Kermit. "That sounds great!"

"What's wrong with the bus terminal?" asked Gonzo. But before he could get an answer, his cage sank.

Soon Kermit, Fozzie, and a soggy Gonzo boarded a red double-decker bus. They told the bus conductor they were going to the Happiness Hotel, then sat down and had their first good look at London.

Kermit stared out the window. The Tower of London . . . Buckingham Palace . . . Big Ben . . . Westminster Abbey . . . London! They had actually made it to London!

The bus turned a corner, and the conductor yelled, "Anyone for the

Happiness Hotel?"

"Yes! We want the Happiness Hotel!" Kermit yelled back.

But the bus didn't stop or even slow down. "Okay!" said the conductor. "Jump . . . NOW!"

Kermit, Fozzie, and Gonzo all jumped. They hit the sidewalk with three thuds. "I'm getting a little tired of these crash landings," said Kermit.

"I like them," said Gonzo. "But then, I'm nuts!"

After dusting themselves off, they took a long look at the Happiness Hotel.

It was a tumbledown wreck of a building whose paint was peeling badly. A few brave weeds, trying to climb the iron rails in front, had given up and died. Stiff gray laundry hung from the second-floor balcony. Beyond the broken windows, twisted blinds clinked in the breeze. Kermit read the dilapidated signs: " 'HAPPINESS HOTEL. IT'S WEIRD, BUT IT'S CHEAP.' Sounds perfect," he said.

They crossed the street and entered the hotel. The dark lobby was covered with dust and cobwebs. Faded pictures dangled from rusty nails and a few threadbare rugs covered the floors. A little white-haired man was sleeping at a dusty wooden desk. He woke up and squinted at the three arrivals.

"Hi," said Kermit, approaching the desk. "We'd like a room, please."

"Really?" asked the registration clerk, surprised.

"Yes. We want to check in," said Kermit.

"Hey!" shouted the clerk, whose name was Pops. "Somebody's checkin' in!"

At the sound of his voice, the lobby of the hotel suddenly sprang to life! The residents of the Happiness Hotel peeked in from behind the warped doors, poked their heads through the banister, and popped up from underneath the broken-down furniture.

"Somebody's checkin' in!" they chorused.

Kermit, Fozzie, and Gonzo saw right away that these were no ordinary creatures. They came in all sizes and colors. There was a brown dog named Rowlf, a blue eagle named Sam, and an orange something-or-other called Scooter. Dr. Bunsen Honeydew told them that he was the resident scientist, and then introduced his assistant, Beaker, who looked like a test tube with hair.

A sleepy looking man with a big grin made his way through the chickens, pigs, and rats to say hello. He was Dr. Teeth, leader of the Electric Mayhem Band.

"The band lives here between gigs," rasped Floyd, the long-haired bass player. "So this time it's been

about what . . . five years?"

Janice, Zoot, and Animal, the other members of the band, nodded. They were all weird, especially Animal. He—or it—had shaggy red hair, a mouth full of teeth, and a very wild look in his eyes.

Kermit, Fozzie, and Gonzo felt instantly at home.

The band welcomed the newcomers with a song and then showed them their room.

There wasn't much to see. The bed sagged and hunks of plaster lay strewn on the dusty floor. The bare light bulb, dangling at the end of a long cord, looked as if it might fall down any minute.

"Not bad!" said Gonzo enthusiastically.

"Look," Kermit yawned, "let's just get a good night's sleep. We have to get up early to interview Lady Holiday."

The other two agreed and they all climbed into the bed. Just as they were settled, the bed flipped up and sandwiched them into the wall, upside down.

"Hey, this is nice!" mumbled Gonzo.

"Can somebody turn out the light?" asked Kermit. As if it had heard, the light bulb shattered to the floor.

"Thanks," said Kermit, and fell asleep.

The next day, Lady Holiday stood in her office talking on the telephone. "Yes, darling," she said. "I'm fine. I had quite a scare. *Of course* the diamonds are valuable. *All* my diamonds are valuable." Tall, neat, stern, and efficient, Lady Holiday was not one to waste time chatting. She quickly hung up the phone and walked briskly among her assistants and models. Under her leadership, they were preparing for the big Holiday fashion show. Unfortunately, things weren't going very smoothly. Some of her new spring designs *still* needed work. A snip here, a dash of ink there, and the famous designer expertly altered several dresses to the appreciative applause of her workers.

Her three top models, Carla, Marla, and Darla, posed, streamlined and elegant, before her. Lady Holiday slowly walked around each one, studying her designs.

"Carla," she said, "the neckline on that gown is too high. You look like an ostrich. And you, Marla, I don't think we should strive for the fan-tailed pigeon look, do you?" Finally, she circled Darla. "That outfit's the pits—like folds on a turkey neck." She dismissed the models with a wave of her hand and sat down at her desk. "Why did I design such awful dresses?" she fretted, shaking her head. "My models look like barnyard animals."

Then came a knock on the door. Lady Holiday wearily looked up. A short figure, dressed in a tailored suit, was standing in the doorway. The visitor's face was hidden by long blond hair and the brim of her hat. But then she slowly raised her head, gazed at Lady Holiday with big, blue eyes, and smiled demurely. This visitor was a pig.

"Good heavens!" gasped Lady Holiday. "Who are you?"

"My name is Miss Piggy," said the visitor. "I would like to be a high fashion model. I've come all the way to London with a single goal in

mind. To meet you—the one and only Lady Holiday." Miss Piggy bounded into the office.

"May I come in?" she asked.

"Absolutely not," answered Lady Holiday.

Miss Piggy plunked her book of fashion photographs on Lady Holiday's desk. "May I show you my portfolio?"

"No," said Lady Holiday.

Miss Piggy quickly turned the pages of the book. Though she wore different clothes in each picture, Miss Piggy was in exactly the same pose, smiling sweetly into the camera.

"Interesting range of emotions," commented Lady Holiday sarcastically.

"Why, thank you," said Miss Piggy. "As you can tell from this small sampling, modeling is my life.

It's my destiny." Miss Piggy paused. "I will accept nothing less."

"Well, I can give you a job as a receptionist," said Lady Holiday.

"I'll take it! I'll take it!" shrieked Miss Piggy, jumping up and down with excitement. "I won't disappoint you," she promised. "I can type. I can take shorthand. I can make coffee. I can do it all!"

"Sit," said Lady Holiday.

Miss Piggy sat. "I can sit," she said. "Sitting is one of my best things."

"Are you quite under control?" asked Lady Holiday doubtfully.

"Cool as a cucumber," Miss Piggy assured her.

"Now," said Lady Holiday, her tone brisk, "I'll be lunching with my brother Nicky. He's second in command here. Unfortunately, he's an irresponsible parasite. He gambles away my money, uses my charge accounts, eats my food, and takes my cars. He's even a little greasy and unsavory and he's certainly not to be trusted. Still and all . . . he's my brother." Lady Holiday sighed. "Anyway," she said, quickly changing the subject, "I want you to answer the phone while I'm away and straighten up the office."

"Consider it done," declared Miss Piggy.

For the first time that day Lady Holiday smiled. "Carry on. I'll be back in an hour," she said. Then she turned and swept out of the room.

The instant the door closed, Miss Piggy jumped up and threw her hat in the air. "Wheee! Oh boy, oh boy, oh boy, oh boy!" she squealed. "I'm going to be a famous model! Oh, Miss Piggy, you are on your way!"

Carla, Marla, and Darla, dressed in trench coats and berets, waited for the elevator near Lady Holiday's office. "Where does Lady Holiday get off calling me an ostrich?" said Carla.

"We'll get even with her tonight when we steal her necklace," hissed Darla. The models thought about the beautiful necklace Lady Holiday would wear to the Dubonnet Club that night. They smiled when they imagined the look on Lady Holiday's face when her precious necklace disappeared.

Then the elevator door opened. "Shhhh," warned Carla.

Gonzo gawked at the three glamorous females. He grabbed his camera to take their picture and the elevator door closed right on his nose.

Fozzie yanked him out. "You okay?" he asked.

"Sure!" said Gonzo cheerfully. "It's just my nose."

"You guys stay here," said Kermit. "I'll try to find Lady Holiday."

Kermit walked down the hall, reading the names on the office doors.

Finally, Kermit reached the door marked "LADY HOLIDAY." He heard a woman's voice and, curious, pushed open the door. There he saw Miss Piggy standing on top of the desk. Her arms were outstretched, as if she were embracing an adoring crowd.

"Thank you, thank you!" she said

to the windows. "Please . . . stop throwing roses! I never dreamed when I started in the business that I'd wind up in such a lofty position. Thank you! Thank you!"

"Excuse me," interrupted Kermit.

Embarrassed, Miss Piggy stopped and cleared her throat. "So, what do you think of the drapes?" she said. "Personally, I'd rather see shutters." Stepping to one side, she continued, "Then on this wall . . . Oops!" Miss Piggy fell right into the wastebasket! She lay in a heap, stunned and groggy.

Kermit rushed to help her. "Lady Holiday! Lady Holiday! Are you all right?"

Miss Piggy opened her eyes. At first all she could see was a green blur. Slowly, the green blur became a fuzzy green face . . . then it became a frog's green face. Finally, everything came into sharp focus and . . . there he stood, the frog of her dreams! Miss Piggy fell madly, hopelessly in love!

"Gee, are you okay?" Kermit was concerned.

"I don't think I'll ever be the same," breathed Miss Piggy. "I don't usually fall like that."

"I thought it was a very nice fall," said Kermit. "Quite graceful, actually."

"Thank you, whoever you are," said Miss Piggy.

"I'm Kermit the Frog," said Kermit. "I've come from America to interview you for the *Daily Chronicle!*"

"Why me?" asked Miss Piggy.

"Because you're Lady Holiday," answered Kermit.

"I am?" Then Miss Piggy realized that this wonderful frog thought she, Miss Piggy, was *the* Lady Holiday. She decided not to disappoint him. "Yes, I am!" she said. "Want to help me out of this wastebasket?"

Kermit helped her up. Miss Piggy gazed at him dreamily through her long lashes. Kermit shyly shuffled his feet. "May I ask you some questions?"

"No, not here," Miss Piggy said nervously. She was afraid the real Lady Holiday would return and spoil everything.

"Perhaps you'd like to have dinner tonight," suggested Kermit.

"Fine!" chirped Miss Piggy. "See you then!"

"Shall I pick you up at your house?" persisted Kermit. "It must be beautiful."

"I'm sure it is," said Miss Piggy. Then she caught herself. "I mean, it *sure* is. Are you kidding? I'm Lady Holiday. I'm not going to live in some pigpen." She leaned back in the chair and put her feet up on Lady Holiday's desk.

"So, where do you live?" asked Kermit.

Miss Piggy, of course, had no idea where Lady Holiday lived. She slowly ran her finger along the edge of the desk.

"Uh . . . guess!" she said, smiling coyly at Kermit.

"Probably some highbrow street somewhere." Kermit shrugged.

"Highbrow Street!" exclaimed Miss Piggy. "Absolutely right! You must be psychic. But what number?"

"I don't know." Kermit was baffled. "Number seventeen."

"Yes, all right," agreed Miss Piggy. "Seventeen Highbrow Street."

They arranged to meet at seven o'clock. Kermit nervously backed out the door stammering, "It was, uh, nice m-meeting me."

"Same here, Sherman," said Miss Piggy.

"Kermit," he corrected her, then walked out the door.

"Kermit," sighed Miss Piggy, "that's a nice name." And in a fit of ecstasy, Miss Piggy fainted and—again—landed in the wastebasket.

Kermit met Fozzie and Gonzo on the steps of the Holiday building and told them all about Lady Holiday. "She's not at all what I expected. She has nice eyes . . . and it might have been my imagination, but I think she found me attractive.

"Taxi!" he cried, waving his arm. Three times he signaled for a cab. No drivers stopped for him. Finally, Gonzo flung himself into the path of a speeding cab and lay spread-eagle on the pavement. A little yellow taxi stopped just short of his head.

"That's very effective," said Kermit.

"Yes, it's great when it works!" agreed Gonzo.

"Where are you guys going?" asked the driver, named Beauregard, Bo for short.

"Happiness Hotel," said Fozzie.

"That's where I'm going! How do you get there?"

"Haven't you ever been there?" asked Kermit.

"Sure, I *live* there," replied Bo. "I just don't know how to *get* there."

"Straight ahead," said Kermit.

"Right," said Bo, suddenly making a U-turn. He drove back in the opposite direction, sometimes on the street, sometimes on the sidewalk. "Takes a while to get to know the town," he confided.

A few seconds later, he said, "Where to?"

"The Happiness Hotel," Kermit reminded him.

"Right," said Bo and made another U-turn. "What's your room number?" asked Bo.

"We're on the second floor," said Fozzie.

"Sorry," said Bo. "I can only take you as far as the lobby."

When they got to the hotel, Bo crashed through the door and stopped in the lobby—just as he had promised.

After the dust settled, Kermit jumped out of the cab, paid Bo, and hurried upstairs to get ready for his

24

big date. While he was shaving, Fozzie stood behind him and kept him company.

"We're going to have some fun tonight, right, Kermit?" asked Fozzie, brushing his fur.

"*We?* What do you mean *we?*" Kermit glared at Fozzie through the broken mirror.

"The two of us," said Fozzie.

Kermit stopped shaving. "Wait a minute," he said, waving his razor in the air. "It's *my* date. Just me. I'm going alone. Me and Lady Holiday. That's it. Not *we. Me.*"

"Oh, I see," said Fozzie. He was hurt.

Kermit put on his tuxedo, gave his cuffs a last tug, his top hat a quick pat, and then admired as much of himself as he could see in the mirror. "Well, how do I look?"

"You look like you're really going to have fun . . . without me," sniffed Fozzie.

Fozzie's eyes drooped. His head drooped. Even his polka-dot tie drooped. Kermit gave in. "Okay, you can come along."

"You mean it?" Fozzie perked up.

"Yeah, but let me do the talking," Kermit warned.

"My lips are sealed!" He trotted to the door and threw it open. "Great news, gang!" he announced. "We can all go!"

Kermit sighed, shook his head, and walked out the door.

Meanwhile, Miss Piggy stood outside 17 Highbrow Street. Her hair was curled and she wore a long, dark cape over a pink sequined evening gown with dainty glass slippers to match. Miss Piggy looked beautiful . . . and worried. How could she make Kermit believe that this elegant home was hers?

She peeked through a window to see who was inside. A very proper-looking couple sat eating dinner in a wood-paneled dining room. They didn't notice the snout pressed against the windowpane.

"Awfully disappointing weather today, don't you think, Neville?" the woman asked her husband.

"Hmmm?" Neville was falling asleep.

"The weather's awfully disappointing today," repeated his wife.

26

"Is it," said Neville absently. Then, "Yes. Yes! I know what you mean, Dorcas. Yes, awfully."

"It was rather disappointing yesterday and the day before," Dorcas droned on.

Just then a strange clanking noise interrupted their exchange. Neville looked out the window.

"What is it, Neville?" asked Dorcas.

"Just a pig climbing up the side of the house," said Neville calmly.

They continued eating.

Miss Piggy was indeed slowly working her way up the drainpipe, glass slippers and all. She climbed toward the eaves that stuck out above the second-floor windows. Three-quarters of the way up, she slipped . . . then regained her balance. When she finally got to the top, she reached out a gloved hand, pitched forward, and grabbed the ledge. Her cape flapped around her legs as she swung back and forth, aiming herself at an open window.

Inside, Dorcas and Neville finished dinner. As they sat talking, there was a loud crash overhead. They ignored it.

Upstairs, Miss Piggy untangled herself from a long cord. She'd climbed through the window with no problems, but then knocked over a large lamp. She listened. No one was coming, so she tiptoed to the top of the stairs. Gathering her cape so that she wouldn't trip, she crept down the stairs and hid. Neville and Dorcas couldn't see her, but she had a clear view of the front door from her hiding place.

Within moments, the doorbell rang. Neville pulled out a gold pocket watch. "Seven o'clock," he said, clicking the watch shut.

"Are you expecting guests?" asked Dorcas.

"Er, no . . . no. Are you, dear?" asked Neville.

"No," answered Dorcas, puzzled.

But Miss Piggy was. She squirmed with excitement. It had to be Kermit!

"Shall I answer it then?" continued Neville.

"Well, I don't know, actually," replied Dorcas.

"I'll answer it," said Miss Piggy, unable to wait any longer. She jumped up and ran to the door.

"Oh, that's quite kind of you," said Neville.

When she opened the door, Kermit gave her a corsage. "For you," he said.

"Well, let's get going," said Miss Piggy. She tried to close the door behind her, but Kermit wanted to see the house. He'd never been inside a real, live English house before. So Miss Piggy grabbed his hand and dragged him into the living room. Neville, bewildered, followed them. With Kermit in tow, Miss Piggy sprinted through the rooms, trying to lose Neville. Desperate to stay out of sight, she detoured Kermit into a closet.

"And this," she said, "is a closet."

"Nice," said Kermit, looking around. "Dark, but nice."

Neville opened the closet door. "Oh, sorry," he said when he saw Kermit and Miss Piggy. "Hope I'm not being rude, but is there anything I can do for you?"

"Uh, yes," said Miss Piggy, trying not to let on that she didn't own the place. "We need the name of a nice restaurant."

"You might try the Dubonnet Club," Neville suggested politely. "Actually, it's more of a supper club than a restaurant, but . . ."

Miss Piggy didn't wait for him to finish. She hauled Kermit out of the closet, down the stairs, and through the front door.

Kermit hadn't noticed that anything was wrong. "I was lucky enough to get the hotel limousine," he told Miss Piggy as they walked toward the street.

The vehicle Kermit so proudly called a limousine was part van, part double-decker bus, and part shed. Pops, the registration clerk, sat behind the wheel, and the Electric Mayhem Band rode on top under a makeshift canopy. Everyone else from the hotel leaned out the windows or clung to the fenders, except for the chickens. They had their own trailer attached to the back.

"Hey, everybody! There they are!" shouted Floyd. "Kermit and his new flame!"

Kermit and Miss Piggy climbed into the front seat. Pops started the engine and the band serenaded Kermit and Miss Piggy all the way to the Dubonnet Club.

The Dubonnet Club, one of London's most elegant night spots, was a round room, all sparkling white and gleaming black. A band was playing romantic music, and a chandelier made of mirrors slowly revolved above, sending twinkles of light onto the swaying dancers.

Miss Piggy, Kermit, Fozzie, and Gonzo sat at a table right next to the glittering dance floor.

Miss Piggy studied the menu while Kermit looked over her shoulder. "Yikes!" he yelped.

"Something wrong, Kermy?" asked Miss Piggy.

"No, no!" Kermit laughed nervously. "It's just amusing that the roast beef is the same price as an Oldsmobile. You . . . uh, eat here often, Lady Holiday?" he asked, his voice cracking.

"Only on special occasions, Kermy," Miss Piggy purred. "And this is very special." She waved to attract a waiter's attention. "Waiter!" she demanded sharply. "Champagne and caviar, s'il vous plaît!"

"How are we going to pay for this?" Fozzie whispered to Kermit.

"Leave it to me," said Gonzo. He hopped down and aimed his camera at a couple sitting next to them. "There you are, folks! Souvenir picture!" he said, blinding them with the flash. "Just give me your name, address, and ten pounds and I'll mail it to you!" The man reached into his pocket and pulled out the money. Gonzo's plan worked! He proceeded to the next table.

At that moment, the real Lady Holiday, dressed in orange satin, entered the club with her brother, Nicky. She stood, head held high, waiting to be shown to a table. Nicky, on the other hand, snapped his fingers and bopped to the music.

Stanley, the headwaiter, greeted

his famous customers. Right away he noticed Lady Holiday's spectacular diamond necklace.

"It is rather breathtaking, isn't it?" agreed Lady Holiday. "I feel a little nervous wearing it, but my brother Nicky insisted."

Stanley led the way to a table near the dance floor. Nicky helped

his sister into the booth, then sat down beside her. "There," he said soothingly, "aren't you happy we're here?"

"I'd be happier if this necklace were locked in a safe," snapped Lady Holiday. "I feel as if thieves are breathing down my neck."

"Nonsense," said Nicky, breathing down her neck.

"Nevertheless," continued Lady Holiday, "I want my jewels put in the safe immediately."

"No!" said Nicky, quickly adding, "I mean . . . of course . . . if that's the way you feel. I'll ask the headwaiter to take care of it."

Nicky got up and went to find Stanley. But once out of his sister's sight, he turned on his heel and scuttled to the back of the club. Glancing over his shoulder to make sure no one was looking, Nicky ducked through a swinging door and walked quickly to the back entrance.

He checked his watch. The models were due any minute now. He unlocked the door so they could get into the club without Lady Holiday seeing them. Then, smoothing his jacket and straightening his bow tie, he re-entered the club, convinced his brilliant plan would work perfectly.

Moments later, a long, dark car pulled into the alley behind the Dubonnet Club. Carla, Marla, and Darla, all dressed in black evening gowns, slid out of the car and pushed open the back entrance to the club. No one but Nicky noticed them come in.

Meanwhile, Kermit and Miss Piggy danced and danced. "Uh, would it be okay if we talked about the jewel robbery?" asked Kermit. His flippers were killing him.

"Oh, Kermy, let's not talk business right now," pleaded Miss Piggy. "There's music in the air, the night is young, and I'm so beautiful. What jewel robbery?"

"Remember your necklace?" asked Kermit. "The one that was stolen?"

"Did anyone ever tell you you have lovely eyes?" cooed Miss Piggy.

Kermit was getting nowhere fast.

The Dubonnet Orchestra struck up another song. Miss Piggy left Kermit and glided over the floor by herself. Everyone stopped to watch the amazing pig dip and swirl to the music. Even Nicky, with crime on his mind, noticed Miss Piggy. As he watched her, he leaned forward in

his seat and for a moment forgot all about his accomplices.

"Nicky!" Lady Holiday suddenly gasped. "That's my new receptionist out there!" She pointed to the dance floor.

"Oh yeah? Which one?" asked Nicky, still gaping at Miss Piggy.

"The pig," answered his sister.

"She's sensational!" panted Nicky.

Entranced by Miss Piggy, he staggered across the dance floor, took her in his arms, and danced with her!

Carla, Marla, and Darla watched Nicky from their posts behind the black pillars on the upper level. They frowned at each other. Nicky falling in love was definitely not part of the plan.

The song finished, and Nicky returned to his seat. He looked at his watch. Not even the most beautiful pig in the world could distract him from his master scheme. Carla gave a signal, Marla threw a light switch, and suddenly the Dubonnet Club was dark. The band stopped playing. Waiters tripped. Dishes crashed.

Then "AIEEEEEEEEEEEEEE!"

Lady Holiday screamed!

The lights came back on.

The headwaiter rushed to Lady Holiday's table. "What happened?"

"Someone stole my necklace!" she exclaimed. She glowered at Nicky. "I told you this would happen! That necklace was worth a fortune. Do something!"

"What do you want me to do?" whined Nicky, secretly delighted. "Look, I just spilled ketchup all over myself."

Kermit, Fozzie, and Gonzo all watched the commotion from the

other side of the room. "Isn't it awful?" said a man passing Kermit's table. "Someone stole Lady Holiday's necklace!"

"Lady Holiday?" said Kermit. "But I thought . . ." He was confused. If that was Lady Holiday over there, then who was . . . ? He turned to ask *his* Lady Holiday to explain, but she was gone! He saw her slipping out the front door. He started to follow, when Gonzo tugged at his sleeve.

"Kermit! Kermit! I got a picture of the thief!"

But Kermit wasn't paying attention. He knelt down and picked up the glass slipper that the mystery pig had left behind. He stared at the slipper, dumbfounded.

The clock struck twelve.

Later that night, in the Happiness Hotel bathroom, Kermit and Fozzie looked over Gonzo's shoulder as he developed his photographs. A line of angry residents pounded on the door. "Open up in there!" they shouted.

"Hurry up, Gonzo," said Kermit. "There's got to be a picture of somebody taking Lady Holiday's necklace."

Gonzo worked fast. A few seconds later, his eyebrows shot up. "Here it is!"

"Wow!" exclaimed Fozzie, squinting at the negative. In the picture, a man was passing the necklace to one of the three women who stood nearby.

"No doubt about it," declared Kermit. "It's that guy sitting next to Lady Holiday and those girls standing around in back."

"It's a whole gang!" said Gonzo.

"And we've got them with their hands in the cookie jar," said Kermit.

Just then, Animal, in a frenzy, broke down the bathroom door. Light flooded into the room and destroyed the negative.

"The cookie jar just broke," sighed Fozzie.

The next day, Kermit sat alone on a park bench. He felt horrible—as if his best friend had moved away without telling him. He couldn't stop

thinking about Lady Holiday, or whoever she was. He turned her glass slipper over and over in his hand and tried to figure out every-thing that had happened. Why had she betrayed him? Did she have something to do with the robbery? *Who was she?*

All of a sudden, Miss Piggy flounced down the path toward the bench. She wore a lavender coat, and this time her curls were tucked up inside a matching hat. She saw Kermit, and pulled up her collar to hide her face. But it was too late.

"Well, well, well, if it isn't the fake Lady Holiday," said Kermit. "What are you calling yourself today, huh?"

Miss Piggy emerged from under her collar. "Hello!" she said cheerfully.

"Hello?" huffed Kermit. "Last night you never even said good-bye. You lied to me."

"Please let me explain," said Miss Piggy. "It's true I'm not Lady Holiday. My name is Miss Piggy. But I am soon to be one of the world's leading fashion models. And I only lied to you because I wanted to be with you."

"Oh yeah?" said Kermit. "Well, I saw the way you were dancing with that guy last night. Let me tell you something. He happens to be a jewel thief!" Kermit stomped off.

"Oh, Kermit, please forgive me," said Miss Piggy. "Please don't go."

Kermit stopped mid-stomp. She sounded so forlorn. . . . He forgave her.

It just so happened they were right next to a Rent-a-Bicycle stand. So Miss Piggy and Kermit spent the rest of the day riding bicycles, making up, and becoming *very good* friends.

The next day was the big Holiday fashion show. Backstage in the mirror-lined dressing room, tall, slim, half-dressed models preened before going onstage. Dressers zipped up zippers, seamstresses stitched hems, and make-up experts searched for missing eyelashes. Hair stylists darted from model to model, twisting a curl on this one, snipping the bangs on that one. Everyone in the room was frantic except Nicky Holiday. He stood calmly in front of a mirror slicking down a strand of dark, greasy hair.

"Okay. We're all set," said Lady Holiday. The big red feather in her red hat bobbed up and down as she gave last-minute instructions. Suddenly, Miss Piggy burst into the room, pushing a rack of clothes. "Gangway! Low bridge! Watch it, sister!" she yelled as she whizzed by.

Nicky watched her every move. "She's wonderful, isn't she?" he murmured.

"She certainly seems to know where she's going," said his sister, straightening her dress. She looked at her watch. "It's time," she said to Nicky. "You better get out there."

Nicky checked himself in the mirror one last time. He was heading toward the stage when Miss Piggy galloped by, carrying a pile of dresses. She ran right into Nicky and he grabbed her. "Have dinner with me tonight," he begged. "Please. From the minute I saw you, you were like a breath of fresh air. I'm tired of the same kind of woman—it's *you* I want!" He tried to kiss her, but Kermit walked in, looking for Miss Piggy.

"Oh, Kermy, I'd like you to meet someone," said Miss Piggy, wriggling out of Nicky's arms. "This is Nicky Holiday. Nicky, this is Kermit, *my special friend.*"

Nicky got the message. He had been aced out by a frog.

Carla, Marla, and Darla watched the whole scene. They cornered Nicky behind a rack of clothes. "You better snap out of it," Carla threatened, ". . . fast!"

"We've got to plant the necklace on Miss Piggy to make sure no one suspects us," Darla reminded him.

"Okay, okay. I'll do my job," said Nicky sadly. "When I give the signal, you do yours." Then, under his breath, he added, "Forgive me, Miss Piggy."

Nicky went through the curtains, grabbed the microphone, and stood in the spotlight on a large runway. Smart designers, wealthy buyers, photographers, reporters, and Kermit, Fozzie, and Gonzo sat in the audience, waiting for the show to begin. Nicky smiled and waved. "And now, Lady Holiday Fashions takes great pride in presenting 'Slink into Summer'! All aboard for the Holiday Line!" He extended his arm toward the curtains. "And here's the captain of the ship, the

hostess with the mostest . . . the one and only Lady Holiday!"

Lady Holiday bowed graciously. She took the microphone from Nicky, who went backstage. "Roses, hyacinths, lilacs, and bluebells make up our first fashion bouquet," said Lady Holiday. An orchestra started to play as three models dressed in pastel chiffon frocks appeared from behind the curtains. They swept down the runway, one at a time, toward a fountain that spewed multicolored jets of water. When each model reached the fountain at the end of the runway, she slowly turned, so that everyone could fully appreciate what she wore. Then she walked back up the runway and disappeared behind the curtains.

Miss Piggy watched the show from the wings. Nicky, seeing that she was occupied, started the next part of the plan. He gave Marla a signal.

Marla instantly fell to the floor. "Oh, my knee!" she moaned, wincing in mock pain. "I've twisted it!"

Miss Piggy heard her moans and scurried to her side. "Oh, you poor thing!" she said. She cradled Marla's head in her arms. "Don't worry. I'll stay right here with you."

"But you can't, Miss Piggy," said Nicky. "*You* have to go on in her place." When Miss Piggy heard this, she dropped Marla's head to the floor like a hot potato.

So far, judging by the enthusiastic applause, the fashion show had been a great success. Beaming proudly, Lady Holiday announced, "And now, the Holiday Swimwear Collection. . . ." The curtains parted and three models stood at the top of the runway. One of them, shorter and a little thicker than the other two, stood in the middle, in the spotlight, her face hidden behind a pleated pink cape. Slowly, slowly she opened the cape to reveal a silver bathing suit, a snout, and two big,

blue eyes. It was Miss Piggy! And she looked stunning! The audience gasped, then rose to its feet. Miss Piggy slowly walked down the runway to thunderous applause!

People cheered while flashbulbs popped all around her! At last Miss Piggy was a famous model! This was the most exciting moment of her life! People loved her! Kermit . . . Nicky . . . everyone! As Miss Piggy floated down the runway, she imagined herself the star in a beautiful water ballet. Nicky and Kermit, backed by a chorus of voices, sang to her: "Oh happiness, Miss Piggy! All the

world's ever wanted was you, a dream come true! Ah, Miss Piggy, it's you! It's you! It's you!"

In the daydream, Miss Piggy made a fabulous arching dive . . . and, in reality, she stepped off the end of the runway into the fountain!

She spluttered to the surface, her hair soaking wet and her pride badly hurt. Everyone rushed to her aid, including Nicky.

But Nicky wasn't planning to help her. He slipped the diamond necklace setting—without the dia-

monds—into her lavender raincoat and then pushed through the crowd. "Here's your raincoat, Miss Piggy, so you won't catch cold," he said.

Miss Piggy waved to show that she wasn't hurt, then put her hand in her raincoat pocket. She pulled out the necklace. "I don't think this belongs to me," she said. She didn't even know what it was.

Miss Piggy had fallen right into Nicky's trap. He turned to Lady Holiday.

"Sis! Do you recognize that?" He

grabbed the necklace away from Miss Piggy and handed it to his sister.

Lady Holiday recognized it immediately. "That's my necklace, but

44

where are the diamonds?" Then she turned on Miss Piggy. "You stole my necklace!" she accused.

Before Miss Piggy could protest, security guards grabbed her. "Wait a minute! I don't have anything to do with this!" She looked at Nicky. "Kermit was right! It was you all the time. You're a phony!" The guards dragged Miss Piggy away.

Reporters crawled around Lady Holiday. "What about the rest of your jewels? What about your most famous jewel, the fabulous Baseball Diamond?"

Lady Holiday was tired of being robbed. She was determined to keep her most valuable jewel out of reach.

"The Baseball Diamond goes on permanent display Monday at the Mallory Gallery," Lady Holiday replied evenly. "I shall never keep it in my possession again."

"That's right," smirked Nicky to Carla, Marla, and Darla. "It'll be in *our* possession." They were listening from behind the curtains. "We'll go to the gallery on Tuesday at midnight," he continued. "And the Baseball Diamond will be ours!"

Little did they know that Gonzo had heard every word.

"So there I was, backstage, under a table, doing a photographic essay on kneecaps, and I heard them planning to steal the diamond," Gonzo later explained to his friends back at the hotel.

"All right," said Kermit, "if we're going to get Miss Piggy out of jail, we're going to have to catch those thieves red-handed."

"What color are their hands now?" asked Beauregard.

Kermit ignored the question and regarded his friends solemnly. "We're about to embark on a dangerous mission. There could be physical violence; there could be gunplay. There's a slight chance that some of us could even be killed. So, if anybody wants out, now is the time to say it."

Everybody wanted out.

"Hold it," said Fozzie, facing the group. "Shame on you. I thought we were in this together. I'm as scared as any of you, but we don't want the bad guys to win." He held his hat over his heart. "We've got to do it for freedom, for justice, for honesty."

No one said a word.

At last, Scooter broke the silence. "Boy, do I feel ashamed."

"Me, too," agreed Pops.

"I'm back in," said Rowlf.

"I was only kidding," chuckled Floyd. "It'll be fun risking our lives."

Before long, every last resident of the Happiness Hotel had volunteered to help out. Kermit and his faithful friends started to make their plans.

Miss Piggy, dressed in drab gray prison clothes, sat alone in her drab

gray jail cell, thinking about her predicament. Just as she was getting to be a famous model, a no-good greasy liar had framed her . . . tricked people into thinking she was a thief. And he'd pretended to love her! Miss Piggy felt betrayed and depressed. Then a guard came to tell her that her lawyer had arrived. "I don't have a lawyer," said Miss Piggy vacantly. She followed the guard to the prison visiting room where she saw a frog in a bowler hat and mustache behind the screen. Miss Piggy burst into grateful tears. "Oh, Kermy, I've missed you!"

"Please," said Kermit stiffly. Then he whispered, "I'm your lawyer. That's the only way they'd let me in."

"Right," said Miss Piggy.

"Listen, we've got a plan," Kermit told her. "We're going to prove you innocent. Tomorrow night at midnight, the thieves are going to steal Lady Holiday's Baseball Diamond from the Mallory Gallery. We're going to stop them!"

"Be careful, Kermy," said Miss Piggy.

"Don't worry. I've got Fozzie, Gonzo, and all our friends from the Happiness Hotel to help," said Kermit.

"Oh no!" groaned Miss Piggy.

Kermit kissed Miss Piggy good-bye through the screen. Then the guard led her back to her cell.

It was Tuesday night. Carla, Marla, Darla, and Nicky—the Holi-day Gang—sat in Nicky's darkened office, huddled over a set of blue-prints to the Mallory Gallery. They all wore matching jet-black jumpsuits. Quickly and efficiently, they went through their check list.

"Glass cutter."

"Check."

"Nylon rope."

"Check."

"Stopwatch."

"Check."

"Computer deprogrammer."

"Check."

It was obviously a smooth, professional operation. When the inventory was finished, the four clasped hands. "Go for it!" whispered Nicky . . . and they went.

At the same time, Kermit and his gang were going over their check list, too.

"Bag of chickens."

"Bawk."

"Frisbee."

"Lost."

"Toothpicks."

"Can't find 'em."

"Wax lips."

"Man, I just had 'em."

"Battery."

"Dead."

It was obviously no operation at all. At the end of their inventory, they clasped hands. "Go for it!" said Kermit. They knocked over the table and clambered out of the room.

Miss Piggy paced her cell. Kermy was about to face those rotten thieves almost single-handed! He might get lost or hurt! Miss Piggy stopped pacing. All of a sudden, she leapt to the bars and, with a surge of super-pig strength, spread them

apart with her bare hands. "Go for it!" she yelled. In the blink of a big, blue eye, she was gone.

The Mallory Gallery, located on the outskirts of town, was a huge rambling building with turrets, domes, and gargoyles. Because the Baseball Diamond was now on display in the gallery's Treasure Room, guards with large, hungry dogs patrolled the grounds.

At exactly 11:27 P.M., a sportscar

with its headlights turned off drove up to the back of the gallery.

At the same time, the Happiness Hotel Courtesy Car, lights ablaze, clanged and clanked up the long front drive.

Back at the prison, a laundry truck rolled out of the gates. Miss Piggy clung to the back, trying desperately not to be seen . . . and not to fall off. When the truck arrived at the laundry, she jumped off. Miss Piggy was free! But how would she get to the Mallory Gallery?

A diesel rig thundered down the road, and Miss Piggy flagged it down. "Excusez moi," she said to the driver. "Do you happen to know where Lady Holiday's Baseball Diamond is being kept?"

"Sure," answered the driver. "It's at the Mallory Gallery, miles away from here."

"How about a ride?" asked Miss Piggy.

The driver pointed to a sign: "NO PASSENGERS."

"Can't you make an exception for little ol' moi?" asked Miss Piggy sweetly.

"No!" said the driver.

Miss Piggy sighed, "I've tried to be nice." Then she flung open the door of the truck, grabbed the driver by the arm, and flipped him over her head into an assortment of garbage cans. The truck was hers! Now to save Kermit!

As the Holiday Gang noiselessly scaled the side of the building and stole across the roof, the Happiness Hotel Gang walked to the front gates. They were cleverly disguised, down to the last chicken. Each wore glasses, a fake nose, and a fake mustache.

Kermit put his hand on one of the solid iron rails. "Okay, Rowlf," he whispered. "Give me the blowtorch."

"Blowtorch?" said Rowlf. "Nobody said anything about a blowtorch. I brought paper towels."

"How are we supposed to cut through this stuff if nobody brought anything to cut with?" Kermit hissed, waving his arms.

"I brought hot mustard," said Floyd, trying to be helpful. "Maybe that'll eat through the bars."

"*Eat* through the bars . . ." Kermit thought fast. "Animal! Come here. See if you can chew through this fence."

Panting heavily, Animal roared and bit a chunk out of the fence. Unfortunately, he didn't roar very softly. Guards and dogs tore around the corner of the gallery and ran across the courtyard toward the gates. Kermit and his friends scattered. Foiling a jewel heist was going to be harder than they thought.

The Holiday Gang pried open a

window and lowered themselves into the gallery. According to their plans, they were one floor above and six rooms away from their goal, the Treasure Room. The four figures slunk silently down a long corridor toward a stairwell.

Outside the gallery, the Happiness Hotel Gang was trying to trick the guard into opening the gates. Kermit and Fozzie, dressed as pizza delivery men, stood at the gates carrying two large, flat boxes. A guard peered suspiciously through the bars of the fence.

"But I never order pepperoni," objected the guard.

"It'sa right here on the slip," insisted Kermit. "Medium pepperoni, double cheese."

The guard opened the gate. He was sure the pizza had been delivered to the wrong address, and he wanted to see the slip. But Kermit

and Fozzie wouldn't show it to him. While they distracted him, the rest of the group sneaked into the courtyard.

A few moments later, after Kermit and Fozzie convinced the guard to give the pizza to his dogs, the Happiness Hotel Gang stood in front of the huge locked doors that led directly to the Treasure Room.

"What do we do now?" asked Gonzo.

"Why don't we ring the bell?" suggested Fozzie.

"There's got to be another way in," said Kermit.

"Well, you better find it fast," warned Scooter. "Those dogs are almost finished with that pizza."

"I know!" said Kermit, pointing toward the sky. "We'll go through the roof!"

His friends craned their necks and looked up the side of the build-

ing. The roof was a long way from the ground—a very long way. "Like man, no way we're going to get up there," said Floyd.

As it turned out, there wasn't much time to discuss the pros and cons. The guard dogs had eaten their pizza and were looking for dessert.

The Happiness Hotel Gang climbed up the wall to the roof in no time flat!

Several miles away, Miss Piggy's truck ran out of gas. She sat by the road. "There's nothing more I can do," she sighed. "It's 11:55. I'll never make it."

But, just then, a van careened out of nowhere and its back door flew open. A motorcycle fell out and gently rolled to a stop right next to Miss Piggy. A helmet and cycling outfit were on the seat. Was it fate? A joke? A stroke of good luck? What did it matter? Nothing could stop Miss Piggy now! She would get to her frog!

The Holiday Gang crept down one last corridor and stood in front of the tall steel door to the Treasure Room. Nicky gave the thumbs-up signal, and the models hooked a little electronic tool to the lock of the door. Nicky pushed a switch and the door swung open. The Holiday Gang stepped over the threshold.

Meanwhile, the Happiness Hotel Gang crowded around a skylight on the roof and looked down into the Treasure Room. The Baseball Dia-mond—the largest diamond in the world—glowed directly below them inside a glass case. They could see how it had gotten its name—it

looked exactly like a transparent baseball, and it was nestled in a red velvet catcher's mitt.

Animal lifted the bars off the skylight. The plan was: wait until the Holiday Gang tried to steal the diamond; then—jump them!

On the highway, the police were chasing Miss Piggy for speeding. Time was running out! She thought about Kermy, and hit the gas.

The Holiday Gang sneaked toward the diamond. They put handles on the protective case and then very, very carefully lifted it. They were nearly home safe.

Kermit, Fozzie, Gonzo, and all their friends watched from above. "How are we going to get down there?" whispered Fozzie nervously.

"I suggest we jump," said Dr. Honeydew.

"It's over a hundred feet!" argued Rowlf.

"I didn't say it was a *good* suggestion," said Honeydew.

Marla and Carla stared at the beautiful stone, transfixed. Nicky snapped his fingers. Darla slowly, cautiously reached for the diamond. She took it out of the velvet mitt and held it in her hand.

"Excuse me," said Fozzie, suddenly appearing upside down in front of Darla's nose, "but I don't think that belongs to you."

Darla looked up and saw that the bear was attached to an extraordinary chain of strange-looking creatures which extended all the way from a hole in the ceiling to her nose! The Happiness Hotel Gang had lowered themselves into the gallery by climbing down each other!

Darla screamed and ran, clutching the diamond in her black-gloved fist.

The Happiness Hotel Gang broke their chain and crashed into action.

"Quick! Throw me the diamond!" ordered Nicky. Darla tossed the diamond to Carla.

Carla threw the diamond to Marla. Marla pitched it back to Darla but it landed right in Animal's mouth. Fozzie slapped him on the back and the diamond flew right into Rowlf's hands.

55

"Heave it over here, baby. Chuck it to me!" yelled Floyd.

Rowlf looked for an opening.

The Happiness Hotel team cheered, "Put some heat on that apple! Let's have it around the horn! They can't hit what they can't see!"

Rowlf threw the diamond to Zoot. It was a high fly and Zoot was out of position! Beauregard intercepted it. "Steeeerike, you're outa there! There's a tater on the pine! Hit the cut-off man!" they urged each other on. Bo heaved the diamond to Kermit. Kermit, his arm stretched high, went back . . . back . . . back . . . he missed! The beautiful jewel landed neatly in the palm of Nicky's hand. Safe!

Carla, Marla, and Darla ran for the door, but found themselves face-to-face with Animal. "Wo-man! Wo-man!" he bellowed.

They surrendered.

Nicky, on the other hand, did not give up. He pulled out a gun and grabbed Kermit. "All right, you guys, back off!" Kermit's friends did as they were told. "Come on, girls," Nicky snarled. "Let's get out of here." He tightened his grip on Kermit's neck and turned toward the window to escape when VVVV-VVVVVVRRRRRRRROOOOOOM-MMMMMMM!!!

Nicky froze. The windowpane shattered! Miss Piggy flew into the room on her motorcycle!

56

She sprang from the bike, landed on Nicky, and knocked him to the floor. The diamond, the gun, and Kermit rolled out of Nicky's reach. Carla, Marla, and Darla, seeing their leader in trouble, scrambled across the room to snap up the diamond.

HIYAAAAA! Miss Piggy met them head on, one against three! A few powerful karate chops and the three models were out of the game.

Nicky recovered from his fall and reached for the gun. Kermit saw him, grabbed the diamond, and bonked Nicky on the head. He was out!

Kermit and his friends had won!

Police and guards burst into the Treasure Room. They pushed past the cheering residents of the Happiness Hotel, yanked the criminals off the floor, and snapped on the handcuffs. The thieves were too stunned to resist. A few shoves and they were out the door on their way to police cars.

Nicky, his hands securely fastened behind his back, staggered past Kermit and Miss Piggy. "I really did care for you, Miss Piggy," he said, reeling. "Please don't hate me."

"I don't hate you, Nicky," replied Miss Piggy. "It's just that somewhere along the line, I found out the difference between wrong and right. You're wrong." She turned to Kermit. "He's right." Kermit blushed.

Everyone was just about to call it a night when Lady Holiday appeared dressed in an orange track suit. "I was jogging past and I noticed a light. What's going on here?" she asked, running in place.

"We just foiled a jewel heist," explained Fozzie.

"And your brother was the thief, not me," added Miss Piggy.

"Nicky, how could you?" scolded Lady Holiday.

"It was easy. I'm no good," admitted Nicky, shrugging.

The police put Nicky, Carla, Marla, and Darla behind bars. The gallery guards locked up the Baseball Diamond, and the Happiness

Hotel heroes congratulated themselves on a brilliant piece of work!

The next day, Kermit and his friends were front-page news. They said good-bye to a grateful Lady Holiday and boarded a plane to go back to America.

In the dim light of the cargo hold, Kermit and Miss Piggy sat side by side on a trunk, talking about Miss Piggy's future as a star. The rats played tag around Sam, and Gonzo flirted with the chickens. Members of the band lounged between mailbags and crates. "Eeeooo,

like somebody laid an egg on my head!" complained Janice.

But, despite the conditions, Fozzie, for one, was happy and proud. He, Kermit, and Gonzo had earned their jobs back! "It was nice of the *Chronicle* to pay for our flight," he said cheerfully.

"Yeah," agreed Pops, "but a man should be treated better than his luggage."

"We don't even have seat belts," Bo pointed out.

"We don't even have *seats*," grumbled Floyd.

A steward interrupted their dis-

cussion. "All out for the U.S.A.!" he announced.

"Oh great!" said Kermit. "How close are we?"

"Oh, about thirty thousand feet," said the steward.

"Kerrrr-mit!" wailed Fozzie.

Kermit gulped. "You mean . . . ?"

"Yep!" chuckled the steward. "Happy landing!" He opened the door and tossed his passengers and their luggage out into the sky, one at a time.

It was a good thing they had parachutes! Everyone drifted safely to the ground and came down right in the middle of the city.

When they had landed, they gathered up the remains of their luggage and went out on the town to celebrate. They deserved it—they were heroes, and they were home!

KERMIT: The best frog in the news-reporting business

LADY HOLIDAY: England's star fashion designer

THE CAST OF CHARACTERS

NICKY HOLIDAY: Lady Holiday's unsavory brother

CARLA, MARLA, and DARLA: Three ambitious models

MISS PIGGY: The most exciting new fashion model in London

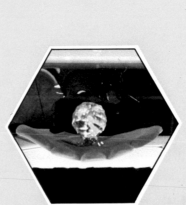

THE BASEBALL DIAMOND: Lady Holiday's prize jewel—the largest diamond in the world

GONZO: A *Chronicle* staff photographer with a nose for news

FOZZIE: Ace reporter, comedian, aspiring detective

MIKE TARKANIAN: Editor-in-Chief of the *Daily Chronicle*